To Jess

I am very grateful to the many friends and colleagues who have contributed to this book.

Professor Mary Gibby

ISBN 978-1-906129-29-3
The Benmore Fernery – Celebrating the World of Ferns

Written by Professor Mary Gibby FRSE

Edited by Anna Levin

Designed by Caroline Muir

Published by Royal Botanic Garden Edinburgh
20A Inverleith Row, Edinburgh EH3 5LR, United Kingdom

Printed by Potts, Northumberland

Built when James Duncan owned the estate in the later part of the 19th century, the Fernery at Benmore had its glory period during the 1870s to 1880s. Now after more than a century of decline and decay it has been beautifully restored thanks to the generous support of the following:

Loch Lomond
& The Trossachs
National Park

Pàirc Nàiseanta Loch Laomainn is nan Tròisichean

The Younger (Benmore) Trust

Sustaining and transforming our heritage

as well as a large number of charitable trusts, organisations and private individuals to whom we express our gratitude.

Cover photos, front and back: Lynsey Wilson/RBGE.

The Royal Botanic Garden Edinburgh is a Charity registered in Scotland (number SC007983) and is supported by the Scottish Government Rural and Environmental Research Analysis Directorate.

Photo: Lynsey Wilson/RBGE.

Foreword

It is a pleasure to write a few words of welcome to this book about ferns, the publication of which marks the successful restoration of the Fernery at Benmore. The Victorians appreciated ferns but today they are often afforded a status below that of the more flamboyant flowering plants. This is unjust for several reasons explained in this book. Ferns are ancient inhabitants of the Earth, dating back many millions of years before more recent arrivals such as the conifers and flowering plants. Whilst they are undoubtedly less showy, their life-cycles are complex and intriguing. Who better than Mary Gibby to write this book in celebration of ferns? Not only is she one of the most accomplished researchers in pteridology – the study of ferns and their allies – she has also championed their conservation and takes an obvious delight in sharing her passion for them with others.

My colleagues and I have long dreamed of being able to open the Benmore Fernery to the public but for many years this seemed impossible. Just five years ago in 2004, when the Board of Trustees of the Royal Botanic Garden Edinburgh (RBGE) met at Benmore Botanic Garden, they lamented the sad state of the lost Fernery, then thought to be beyond hope of repair. Too little information was available on how the Fernery had been constructed, and it was uncertain how robust the remaining stonework was or whether a satisfactory modern roof could be procured. Most of all, it was feared that the cost would be prohibitive. How glad I am that despite the challenges the dream did not die! When the Trustees met again at Benmore in 2007, a plan had been hatched and a budget drawn up. The vision of restoring the Fernery and opening it to the public captured the imagination of many people and, as is often the case once a good plan exists, the obstacle of funding the work proved surmountable. I would like to thank everyone who supported the project and especially the Trustees of the Younger (Benmore) Trust for their unbridled enthusiasm and generous investment, particularly during the vital early stages. The Fernery greatly enhances the interest and variety of one of Scotland's great gardens. I hope that it will also serve to attract new visitors to an outstandingly beautiful part of the country: Loch Lomond and The Trossachs National Park.

Stephen Blackmore FRSE
Regius Keeper
Royal Botanic Garden Edinburgh

Above and top right:
Photos: Lynsey Wilson/RBGE.

Introduction

I was brought up in a small rural village near Cockermouth in Cumbria. My love of plants started in primary school in the nature ramblings led by Mrs Ostle, the infant teacher. From the age of eight I was able to run free in the lanes and woods with my friend Margaret, hunting for primroses and wild violets in the spring, making dens in the summer and foraging for nuts and berries in the autumn. By the time I reached the sixth form I knew I wanted to study botany at university.

The University of Leeds Botany Department was then led by the inspirational professor Irene Manton, the leading expert on fern cytology. Ferns were high on the agenda at Leeds, including work on the ferns of Sri Lanka, evolutionary studies in *Asplenium* and *Polystichum* and even including the fossil ferns of the Yorkshire Jurassic. There was also plenty of opportunity for fieldwork, locally in the Yorkshire Dales as well as residential field courses in the Lake District and Julian Alps (Slovenia). It was during these field courses that my mentors opened my eyes to the diversity of ferns, and I decided that ferns would be the focus of my PhD.

Just before finals I heard of an opportunity to take up a summer studentship at the Natural History Museum in London, working on *Dryopteris*. What could be better! The studentship began with the Museum's Head of Ferns Clive Jermy collecting me from home to head north to Scotland for two weeks' fieldwork. We started in the lush woodlands of Kintyre and Knapdale and worked our way north to Loch Awe, hunting for *Dryopteris carthusiana, D. dilatata, D. expansa* and hybrids, before heading east to join a small group from the British Pteridological Society (BPS) in an exploration of Ben Alder.

The BPS group included the secretary and treasurer, Jimmy Dyce, an enthusiastic Scot who introduced to me the world of fern varieties and the delights of sipping malt whisky; and so a passion for ferns was born. Their alternation of generations, hybridisation and reticulate evolution fascinate me as a scientist, whilst their subtle colour and exquisite form – particularly the unfurling of the fronds – please the eye.

Mary Gibby is Director of Science at the Royal Botanic Garden Edinburgh and president-elect of the British Pteridological Society.

Below: Mary examining ferns in Benmore Botanic Garden. Photo: Vlasta Jamnický/RBGE.

What is a fern?

Ferns – celebrated for their glorious architecture, from stately tree ferns and elegant shuttlecocks to delicate filmy ferns and small, neatly splayed rock ferns, all gracefully unfurling their fronds to display a diversity of patterns. And in a hundred and one different shades of green!

Ferns have a long history, with the oldest fern fossils dating back to the early Carboniferous period some 340 million years ago, even before the appearance of the dinosaurs, but most of the fern families we recognise today appeared much later, during the late Cretaceous period, when flowering plants were already well established. Ferns flourish in humid, shaded woodland, and so can be found as a significant component of the vegetation in temperate and tropical forest, growing as part of the ground flora or as epiphytes on the branches of trees, or scrambling over rocks, boulders and tree boles. They are frequent beside running water and in the splash zone of waterfalls, and some species thrive in bogs and fens. Other ferns grow in rock crevices, under overhangs or clinging to cliffs. Their roots penetrate deeply into cracks in the rocks and such plants often have quite specific requirements, being either strict lime-lovers – calcicoles – or confined to acid rocks. A few species have the ability to grow on serpentine rocks, and other rocks or soils rich in heavy metals. In the absence of natural substrates, lime-loving species will colonise mortared walls. Some species can tolerate periods

A familiar fern

One fern in Britain had a vital role in country life. William J. Hooker in 1821, then Regius Professor of Botany at the University of Glasgow, wrote in *Flora Scotica* that bracken (*Pteridium aquilinum*) was "Used as litter for cattle, and very frequently for the purpose of thatching cottages. The ashes are employed in the manufactories of soap and glass. Its astringent quality has been recommended in the dressing and preparation of kid and chamois leather; the country people take it medicinally, to destroy worms, and a bed made of the green plant is esteemed a sovereign cure for the rickets in children." The fern that today is viewed as a scourge of rough pasture in upland fells and mountains was then a valuable agricultural commodity.

Above: *Gathering Bracken* by Henry Herbert La Thangue (RA), 1899. Courtesy of Laing Art Gallery, Tyne and Wear Archive and Museums.

Right: Rock ferns in the Edinburgh Garden – maidenhair spleenwort (*Asplenium trichomanes*) (left) and rusty-back fern (*Asplenium ceterach*) (right). Photo: Mary Gibby/RBGE.

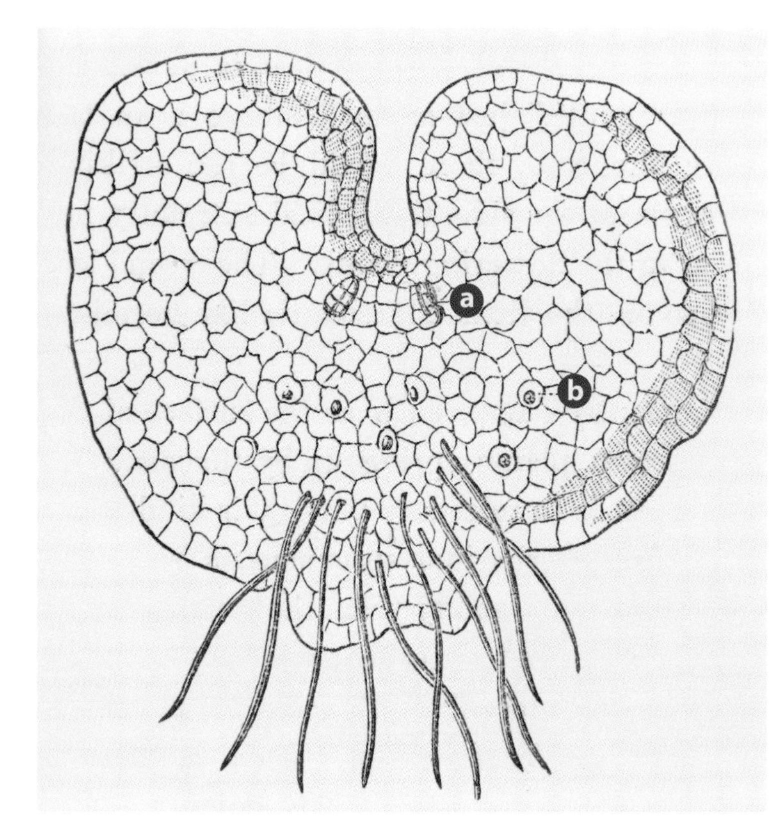

of drought and have developed methods for retaining moisture, with a dense covering of hairs or scales and the ability to curl up during dry weather to retain moisture.

Mystery and folklore developed around ferns. Where were the flowers? Where was the seed? 'Fern seed' was believed to bestow magical properties, conferring invisibility on the bearer – according to Shakespeare, "we have the receipt of fern seed, we walk invisible" (*Henry IV*, Part 1). Or on St John's Eve at midnight it was believed that the fern would flower and release its invisible seed; John Parkinson wrote in his herbal *Theatrum Botanicum* in 1640, "The seede which this and the female ferne doe beare, and to be gathered only on Midsummer eve at night with I know not what conjuring words."

The great Swedish botanist and natural historian Carolus Linnaeus, who established the system for naming and classifying organisms that is still in use today, championed the importance of sex in plants – the form and structure of flowers – for plant classification in his *Systema Naturae* (1735). But ferns, lacking flowers, were an enigma; understanding of their biology and method of reproduction proved difficult and was not fully understood until over a century later.

Top: The fern gametophyte – a prothallus, showing female sex organs (a) and male antheridia (b), from John Smith and Thomas Moore, *An Account of Exotic Cultivated Ferns, General Hints on their Culture, Synopsis of Genera and Species*, (Polypodiaceae grammatis *to* Platyloma), 1858.

Inset: Interrupted clubmoss (*Lycopodium annotinum*). Photo: Heather McHaffie/RBGE.

Right: *Marattia werneri*. Fossils related to this group of ferns date back to the Jurassic period. Photo: Lynsey Wilson/RBGE.

Fern allies

The so-called fern allies include several groups of plants that, like ferns, have water-conducting vascular tissue and reproduce by spores. These are the horsetails (*Equisetum*), whisk ferns (*Psilotum* and *Tmesipteris*), the clubmosses (*Lycopodium*, *Lycopodiella* and *Huperzia*), the spikemosses (*Selaginella*) and quillworts (*Isoetes*). Like the earliest ferns these groups date back to the early Carboniferous period. They were all believed to be closely related to ferns and were classified with ferns as the pteridophytes. Recent research, however, has shown that the horsetails and whisk ferns group with ferns, whereas the clubmosses, spikemosses and quillworts had a completely distinct evolutionary history.

Main: The royal fern (*Osmunda regalis*) in June. Mingulay, Outer Hebrides. Photo: Mary Gibby/RBGE.

John Lindsay, a British surgeon in Jamaica who had received botanical training in Edinburgh from RBGE's Regius Keeper John Hope, demonstrated in 1794 that the dust from the underside of fern fronds grew into "a membranous substance like some ... small liverworts ... dark green in colour", and that ultimately these would produce new fern plants. We now refer to these structures as prothalli or, in the singular, a prothallus. But Lindsay was unaware that the 'dust' was not actually seed but consisted of hundreds of single-celled spores; it was not until the mid-nineteenth century that the fern life cycle was fully understood. In 1844 the Swiss botanist von Naegeli studied these heart-shaped, membranous prothalli (or gametophytes) under his microscope and observed small projections on the underside that, when wetted, released tiny spiral-shaped swimming cells, now called the antherozoids or the 'male' gametes. Later, in 1848, Leszczyc-Suminski, a Polish botanist, found that the spiral antherozoids swam to another small protruding structure close to the notch of the prothallus. This was the archegonium, a structure with an elongated neck and large basal cell – the 'egg' cell or 'female' gamete that, when fertilised by the antherozoid, gave rise to a new frond-bearing sporophyte, the fern. The life cycle had been discovered.

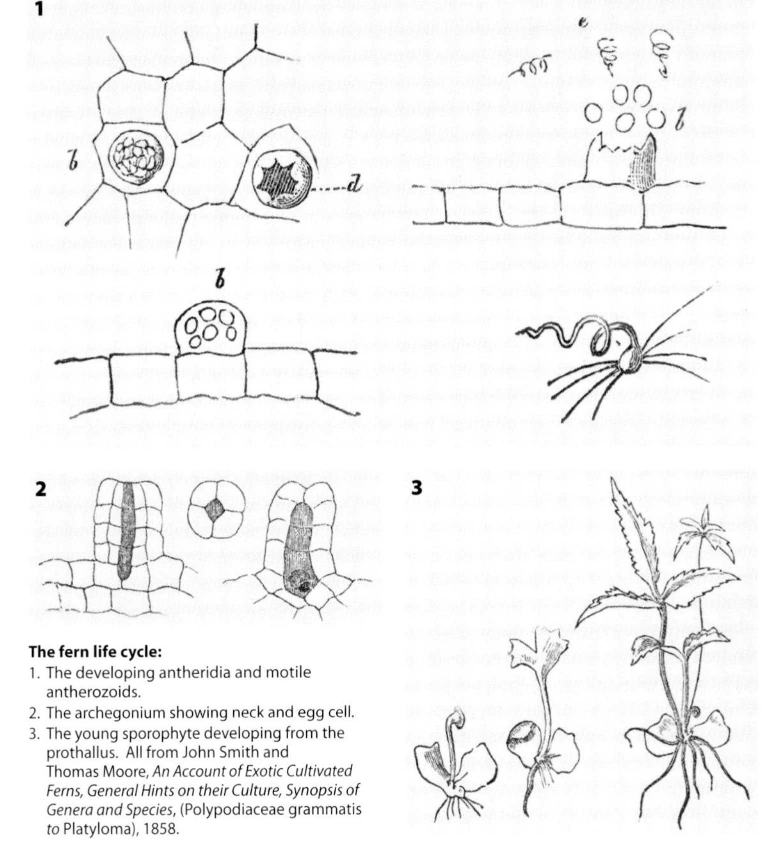

The fern life cycle:

1. The developing antheridia and motile antherozoids.
2. The archegonium showing neck and egg cell.
3. The young sporophyte developing from the prothallus. All from John Smith and Thomas Moore, *An Account of Exotic Cultivated Ferns, General Hints on their Culture, Synopsis of Genera and Species*, (Polypodiaceae grammatis *to* Platyloma), 1858.

The ability to cultivate ferns from spores was a major breakthrough. Although Lindsay had described propagation from spores in 1794, it was probably John Shepherd, Curator of Liverpool Botanic Garden, and his nephew Henry, who first used the method successfully on a large scale. The botanic garden had been established in 1800 through patronage by owners of shipping companies of this great port, and their ships were a major conduit for the importation of plants from across the empire. Captain William Bligh, who in the mutiny on the *Bounty* had been set adrift in the ship's launch with a small crew, on a subsequent voyage went on to transport breadfruit successfully from Tahiti to the West Indies. On his return to Britain he imported some 37 different species of tropical fern. In the late eighteenth century it was a huge challenge to keep such plants alive. Some twenty years later, however, when Sir James Edward Smith, the founder and first president of the Linnean Society, visited the Liverpool Botanic Garden in 1818, he reported finding over 50 exotic species in cultivation, raised from spores by the skills of Henry Shepherd.

Commercial nurseries soon adopted the method of spore propagation and in 1828 Loddiges and Sons of Hackney were able to offer for sale 80 different exotic ferns, and had over 100 in cultivation. Loddiges were also at the forefront of the development of stovehouses, vast steam-heated glasshouses like their Grand Palm House, where in the early 1830s superb collections of orchids, palms and ferns were "in most vigorous growth".

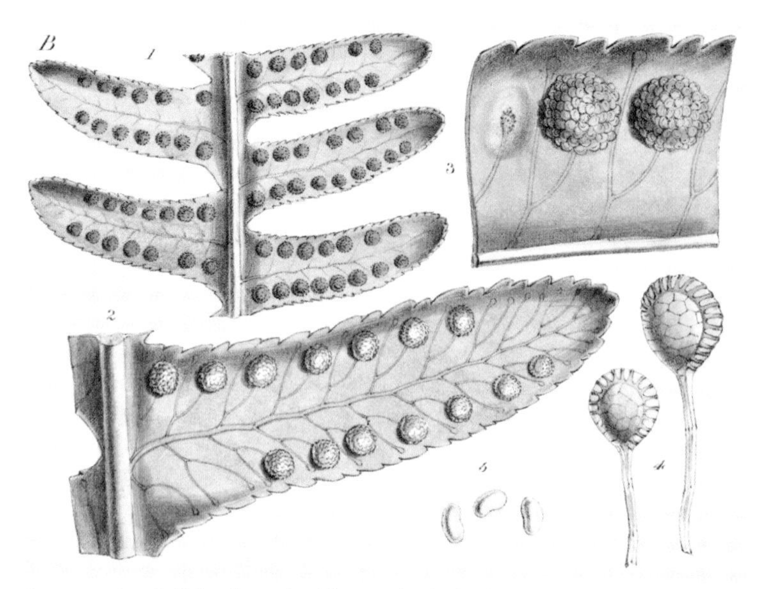

Common polypody (*Polypodium vulgare*) has round, naked sori.

Hard shield fern (*Polystichum aculeatum*) has round sori with peltate indusia.

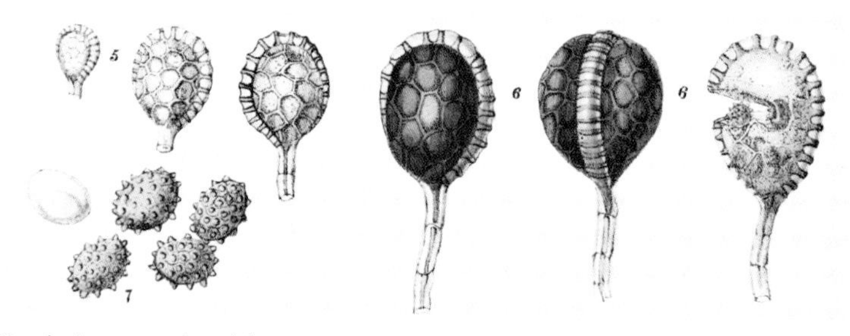

Developing sporangia and ripe spores.

The language of ferns

Special words are used to describe a fern plant. The 'leaf' is not the exact equivalent of the leaf in flowering plants as in ferns this structure bears spores on the underside; it is usually referred to as a frond.

The stem of the frond is referred to as the stipe, with the frond's central 'stalk' being termed the rachis. The stipe grows out from the fern's rhizome; the rhizome may be quite a massive structure as seen in some old plants of the male fern (*Dryopteris filix-mas*) or may be more slender and creeping, as in the polypody (*Polypodium vulgare*). The male fern and ostrich fern (*Matteuccia struthiopteris*) produce a magnificent new shuttlecock of fronds each springtime, which develops from the crown of the rhizome, whereas the fronds of the polypody emerge individually along the length of the rhizome. Bracken has a creeping and very extensive underground rhizome and the fronds erupt from the ground individually.

Many ferns have scales or hairs liberally covering the base of the stipe, and in the unfurled crosier, these scales can be seen to be enveloping the whole structure, protecting the young tissue from damage. The scales or hairs vary in size, shape and colouring, and so provide a useful diagnostic feature when trying to distinguish species.

Fronds themselves vary enormously in the degree of division. The hart's tongue fern (*Asplenium scolopendrium*) has a simple, undivided frond.

Left: Illustrations by Bauer and Fitch from William J. Hooker, *Genera Filicum*, 1838-1842.

In contrast, the black spleenwort (*Asplenium adiantum-nigrum*) is thrice-divided, or tripinnate, where the pinna (plural, *pinnae*) is the first division of the frond. Where the pinna is divided again, the segments are called pinnules; in the black spleenwort the pinnules are subdivided yet again into smaller stalked segments, so that the whole frond appears as a series of fractals, repeating patterns of division. Fern fronds vary in their dissection from simple to many times pinnate.

The dust-like spores develop on the underside of the frond in discrete structures known as sori (singular, sorus). The form of the sorus varies between different groups of ferns. In the polypodies (genus *Polypodium*) the sorus is naked, it has no protective covering, and consists just of many clustered sporangia – the stalked, rounded structures that contain the spores. In contrast, the shield ferns (genus *Polystichum*) have a round sorus with a peltate or shield-shaped indusium attached at the centre that arches over the young sporangia and protects them as they develop.

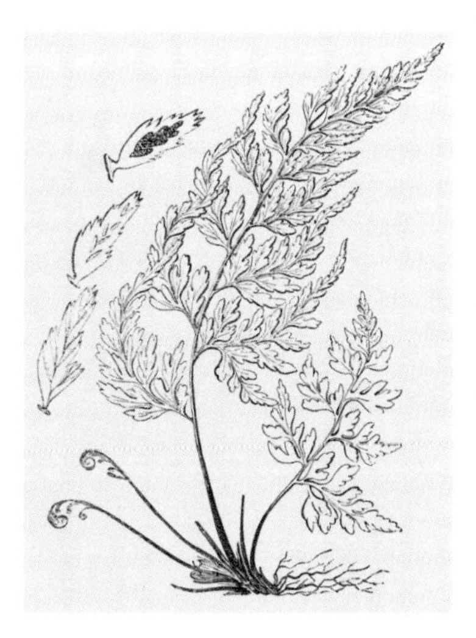

Only when the spores are approaching maturity does the indusium lift around the margins, so that the spores can be liberated from the sporangia. The position and form of the sorus, and presence or absence of indusium, are critical features that have been used in fern classification.

The dramatic release of the spores can be viewed under a hand lens or low-powered microscope. The single-celled spores develop inside the sporangium and, when the spores are ripe, the sporangium loses moisture and ruptures, bursting open and flinging the spores into the air. Many fall to the ground, close to the parent plant, but others may be carried by air currents high into the atmosphere, to be dispersed far and wide.

Top: Ripe spores bursting out of the sporangia of southern polypody (*Polypodium cambricum*). Photo: Heather McHaffie/RBGE.

Bottom left: Woodcut of tri-pinnate black spleenwort (*Asplenium adiantum-nigrum*) from Edward Newman, *A History of British Ferns*, 1840.

Inset: Unfurling crosier. Photo: Lynsey Wilson/RBGE.

Ferns unfurled

Young fronds develop as tightly curled crosiers or 'fiddleheads'. Every segment of each frond is itself curled in a tight spiral, and when the young frond unfurls these many spirals slowly open and expand; this feature – technically called circinate vernation – is one of the key characteristics of ferns.

The Victorian passion for ferns

This page, main: The drawing room at Brodick Castle, Isle of Arran circa 1880. Reproduced with kind permission from Lady Jean Fforde.

This page, above: Mauchline fernware from the author's collection. Photo: Lynsey Wilson/RBGE.

Facing page, top: John Hutton Balfour, circa 1855. Photo: RBGE archives.

Facing page, bottom: An illustration showing a group collecting ferns from the *Illustrated London News*, of 1871. Courtesy of Mary Evans Picture Library/*Illustrated London News*.

The term 'pteridomania' – the fern craze, fern madness – was coined in 1855 by Charles Kingsley, clergyman, naturalist and later author of *The Water-Babies*, to describe the fascination for ferns that was gripping the nation. There was a widespread focus on ferns, whether through cultivation of ferns, fern ramblings, fern collection, identification and exchange; ferns British or exotic, fern varieties, and a great deal of associated paraphernalia. What had sparked such enthusiasm for this relatively insignificant group of plants? What was happening at this period during the early years of Queen Victoria's reign that provided conditions for pteridomania to flourish?

By the Victorian era, the techniques of fern cultivation were well established. There was increasing interest among the British public in natural history and, with improving transport links, there was greater access to the countryside.

In 1836, the year before Victoria ascended the throne, two Botanical Societies were established, the Botanical Society of London and the Botanical Society of Edinburgh. John Hutton Balfour, who in 1845 was appointed Regius Keeper of RBGE and Regius Professor of the University of Edinburgh, played a significant role in widening the appeal of botany at this period. The Botanical Society of Edinburgh had its foundation at a meeting held in his Edinburgh home, 15 Dundas Street, on 8 February 1836, with the aim of holding meetings, establishing a public herbarium and botanical library, providing a centre for the exchange of botanical specimens for "the extension and improvement of private herbaria", publishing reports and plant catalogues, and organising botanical excursions in the local neighbourhood and to "distant parts of Britain".

At this time botany had been introduced "as a branch of female education" and ladies were actively encouraged to become members of the Society. After only one year the Society had acquired, gathered by its members, some 60,000 herbarium specimens representing 1,400 British species and 2,000 exotics. The Society's herbarium comprising many thousands of specimens was donated to the Royal Botanic Garden Edinburgh in 1863, with its valuable library following in 1872.

In 1842 we find Balfour, while Regius Professor at the University of Glasgow, reporting that "the facilities afforded by railway and steam enabled us to visit many interesting localities at a considerable distance from Glasgow", and he describes botanical exploration of the islands of Bute and Arran (via the Ayr railway and the steam boats from Ardrossan), and to Tarbert beside Loch Lomond. The first successful steam passenger railway had been opened between Liverpool and Manchester in 1830, to be followed by a huge programme of railway building over the next 20 years.

Botanical forays were very popular as they presented an opportunity for the novice to learn from the more experienced botanists. The participants were keen to record the species growing in a particular area, with the possibility of finding species not previously discovered in Britain. Samples were collected for the herbarium, to confirm names and make exchanges, and the legacy of these forays is preserved today in the Herbarium at RBGE.

Ferns were an area of botany ripe for investigation, with their 'hidden' life cycles and relatively few characters by which the different species could be distinguished. This was in contrast to the showy reproductive organs of flowering plants that provide a huge array of characters with which to differentiate and classify. The passion for ferns was

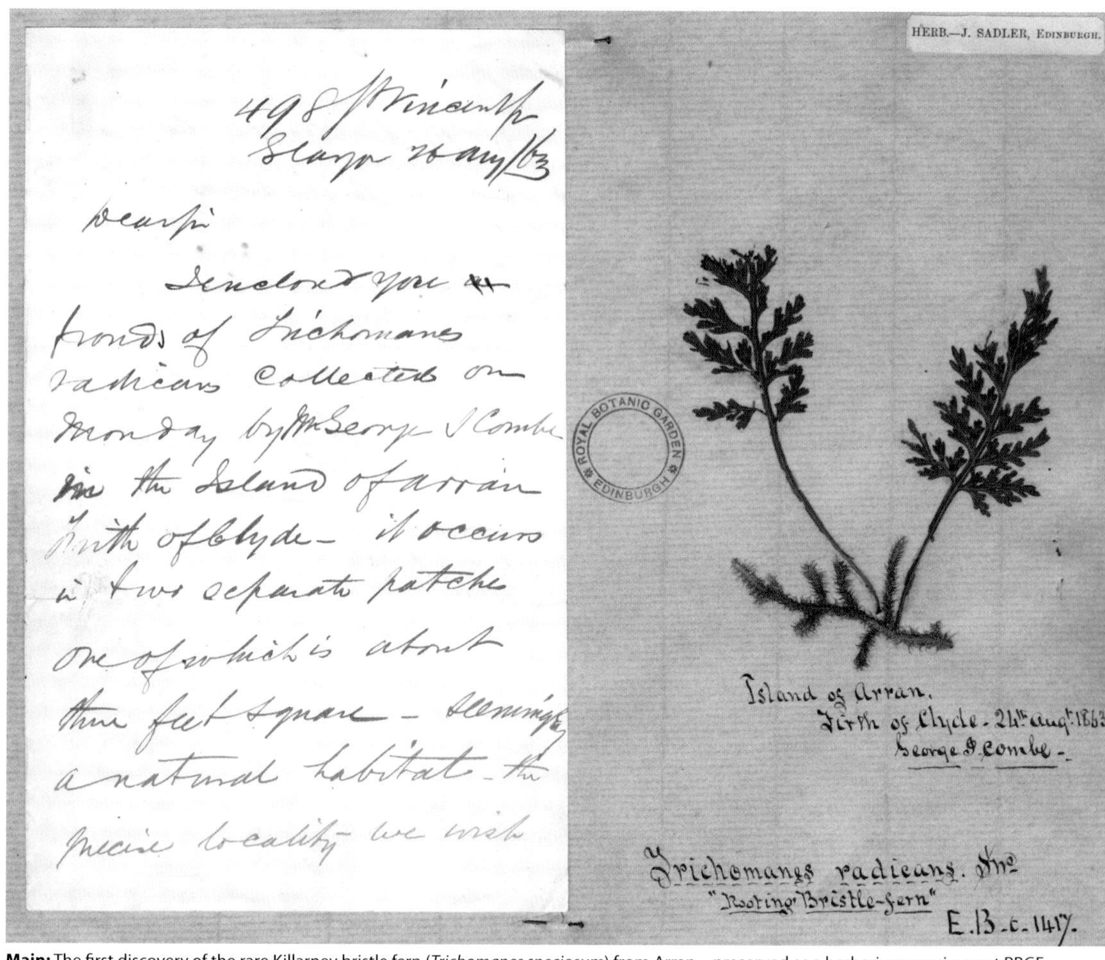

498 St Vincent St
Glasgow 26 Aug/63

Dear Sir

I enclose you ** fronds of Trichomanes radicans collected on Monday by Mr George S Combe in the Island of Arran Firth of Clyde – it occurs in two separate patches one of which is about three feet square – seeming a natural habitat – the precise locality we wish

Main: The first discovery of the rare Killarney bristle fern (*Trichomanes speciosum*) from Arran – preserved as a herbarium specimen at RBGE.

Below: Victorians considered the ornamental Wardian case to be ideal for the cultivation of the Killarney bristle fern. Illustration from John Birkenhead, *Ferns and Fern Culture*, 1892.

part of a trend away from the bright, gaudy colour of flowers, towards a love of intricacy, delicacy, shape and form; they were described as "objects of exquisite elegance", and linked with a love of things gothic.

Fern cultivation was given a boost through an invention by Nathaniel Bagshaw Ward, a London apothecary and member of the Royal College of Surgeons. Like all apothecaries he was trained in botany, and in 1833 he was appointed to the committee of Chelsea Physic Garden, the garden of the Society of Apothecaries. He experienced difficulty in cultivating plants in the smoggy air of London and experimented with a self-sustaining, closed system, to protect plants from the growing pollution. This took the form of a miniature glasshouse – the Wardian case. Specimens were planted into suitable moist compost in the case and this was then sealed, preventing loss of humidity, keeping out noxious fumes and recycling nutrients within the system. Its use, however, was rapidly extended for the transportation of plants and it was critical to the development of the tea industry in India. In 1848 Robert Fortune left his position as Curator of the Chelsea Physic Garden to smuggle tea seedlings from China to India in Wardian cases. The invention continued to be used for plant importation across the seas until the 1950s, when airfreight took over. Meanwhile, the Wardian case found its niche in the drawing rooms of industrial cities around Britain, where ferns could be grown and displayed, safe from the fumes of smoke and smog. A fern case could be as simple as a bell jar, or take on ever more elaborate forms as a casket or an elaborate structure, mimicking the grand glazed palm houses. According to John C. Loudon writing in the *Gardener's Magazine* in 1834, some of the best examples of Wardian cases were to be found at Wellclose Square, in the home of Ward himself, where his drawing room was filled with a profusion of fern cases.

Illustrations by Bauer and Fitch from William J. Hooker, *Genera Filicum*, 1838-1842.
Left: *Culcita macrocarpa*, from the Azores and Madeira.
Right: Tunbridge filmy fern (*Hymenophyllum tunbrigense*).

New techniques in publishing helped to widen scientific and public interest in ferns. William J. Hooker, Director of the Royal Botanic Gardens, Kew from 1841-1865, had specialised in cryptogamic plant groups – mosses, liverworts and ferns – whilst Regius Professor in Glasgow. About the time of his appointment to Kew he published *Genera Filicum*, a work on fern classification with magnificent hand-coloured illustrations by two great botanical artists, Francis Bauer and Walter Fitch. Bauer was first employed by Sir Joseph Banks as Kew's botanical artist. In 1788 he travelled to England and settled at Kew where he was to remain for the rest of his life. Fitch had been apprenticed to a firm of Glasgow calico designers, but Hooker became aware of his skills as a draughtsman when he assisted in the herbarium at Glasgow, and so when Hooker was appointed to Kew he took Fitch with him. *Genera Filicum* was issued in parts between 1838 and 1842. Hooker went on to publish his magnum opus, the five volumes of *Species Filicum*, over the next 20 years. And, responding to the interests of the wider public, he also produced lavishly illustrated popular books, *A Century of Ferns* covering a selection of 100 exotic ferns, and *Garden Ferns* on exotic ferns for the grower.

Edward Newman was a gentleman naturalist and businessman who was a co-founder of the Entomological Society of London. He regularly wrote papers on natural history and in 1832 became editor of *The Entomological Magazine*. He visited Wales in 1837 and made a large collection of ferns; on his return home he "set to work, expecting to name them without difficulty … but could only be certain of two species" – bracken and the common polypody! This inspired him to produce in 1840 *A History of British Ferns*, one of the first popular books on British ferns, and of which he was both author and illustrator.

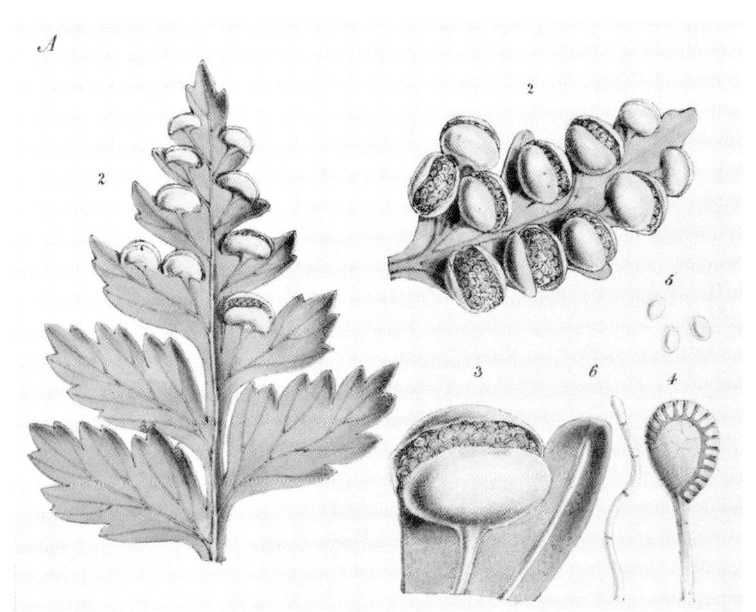

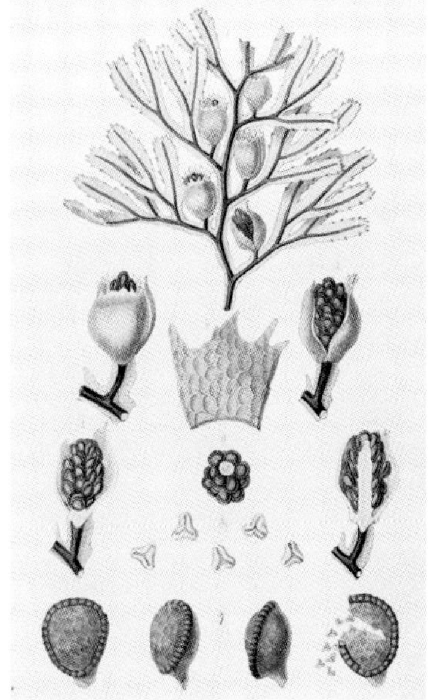

This had immediate success and, following feedback from readers, two more issues with corrections and additions appeared the same year. In 1844 a second edition of *A History of British Ferns, and Allied Plants* had a great number of additions including the fern allies – horsetails and clubmosses. Not only was Newman an author, he was also a publisher, and he established a new journal, *The Phytologist*, that "owes its existence to the desire of recording and preserving FACTS, OBSERVATIONS and OPINIONS relating to Botany in general, but more especially to British Botany".

The confusion and complexity of names and classification added to the delight of fern study. The male fern (now with the Latin name *Dryopteris filix-mas*) is a common plant and would have been very familiar to the Victorian fern enthusiast. But a huge variety of names were applied to this species. Ferns were a challenge for Linnaeus – with no flowering parts to aid classification, many of them were assigned by him to the genus *Polypodium*, with the male fern named *Polypodium filix-mas*. Subsequent botanists sought to produce a more detailed classification for ferns. In the 1850s British botanists were using several different generic names for the male fern: Swartz's name *Aspidium* was used by Hooker at Kew, Charles Babington, Professor of Botany at Cambridge followed Presl's generic name *Lastrea*, and Newman himself erected a new genus, *Lophodium*. Luckily they all used the same specific epithet, *filix-mas*, a name that dates back to pre-Linnean times and had been used in herbals. In applying the term 'pteridomania', Charles Kingsley captures the essence of it: "Your daughters, perhaps, have been seized with the prevailing 'Pteridomania', and are collecting and buying ferns, with Ward's cases wherein to keep them (for which you have to pay), and wrangling over unpronounceable names of species (which seem to be different in each new Fern-book that they buy)."

Newman was to have a competitor in the field of popular books on British ferns. Thomas Moore, horticulturist by training, curator of Chelsea Physic Garden from 1848-1887 and a close associate of Nathaniel Ward, published *A Handbook of British Ferns* in 1848. This book, illustrated with woodcuts, was intended to be a guide to those interested in growing ferns, and provided "scientific and popular

Left: Nature print by Bradbury and Evans of the male fern (*Dryopteris filix-mas*) from Thomas Moore, *The Ferns of Great Britain and Ireland*, 1855-6.

Right: The Victorians delighted in collecting fern varieties like these three hart's tongue ferns. From Edward J. Lowe. *Fern Growing*, 1895.

Below: Three popular pocket-sized books on British ferns by Edward Newman (left), Thomas Moore (centre) and Joachim Otte (right).

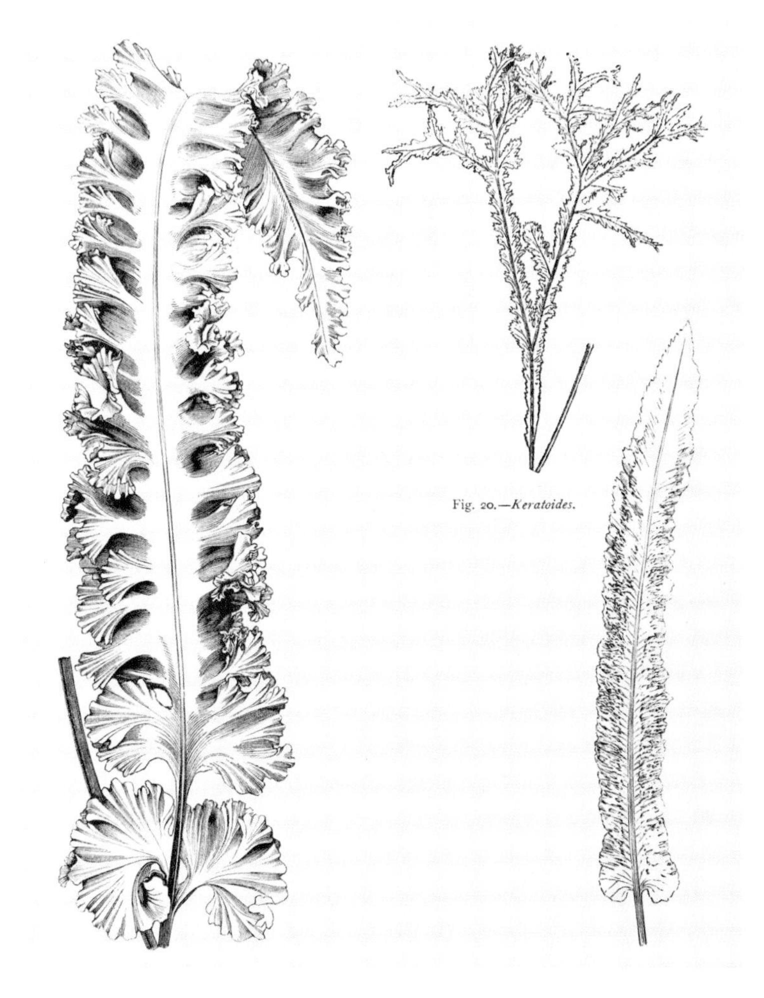

descriptions, with engravings of all the species indigenous to Britain, with remarks on their history and cultivation", and ran into several later editions. It was closely followed in 1851 by *A Popular History of the British Ferns and The Allied Plants comprising the Club-mosses, Pepperworts and Horsetails*. This was aimed at beginners and had clear colour plates drawn by Fitch. It proved very successful and was re-issued, revised and abridged many times.

Moore's greatest work must be *The Ferns of Great Britain and Ireland*, a magnificent folio work illustrated with nature prints by Bradbury and Evans, originally published in monthly parts during 1855 - 1856. *The Phytologist* described it as "One of the most magnificent contributions to British botany". Nature printing involved using a real specimen that was pressed to form an impression on a soft lead plate. From this an electrolytic copper replica was made and this could then be hand inked in colours to produce stunning, totally life-like images. Bradbury had published a shorter series of nature prints the previous year that included both flowering plants and ferns, and a rare set of these plates, including four ferns, is in the Library collection at RBGE.

Moore's *Octavo nature printed British Ferns* (1859 - 1860) included fern varieties as well as species. These varieties were wild mutants – beautiful or bizarre, and the Victorians loved them. Perhaps one of the most extraordinary was a variety of the lady fern found beside a road in Stirlingshire by James Cosh in 1861, and named var. *Victoriae*, "a queen amongst lady ferns", according to John Sadler, curator at RBGE; he also recorded that, remarkably, it had been left in place for two years after its first discovery, before it was removed for cultivation.

Fern cultivation became a passion for Victorians. The wealthy followed the examples of the nurserymen and botanic gardens by establishing their own ferneries, with the Fernery at Benmore being built in the early 1870s and another fernery at Ascog on the island of Bute shortly afterwards in 1878. These two ferneries, both listed buildings and now restored, are a testament to the passion for ferns that was embracing the country. Many more ferneries were developed in other gardens and estates in Scotland, including a further two now listed ferney ruins at Hospitalfield, Arbroath and Newbattle Abbey, south of Edinburgh, but others have been lost without trace. People with limited means could cultivate ferns indoors in simple glazed Wardian cases. Hardy ferns could be grown outside in specially constructed fern gardens, but always the goal was to try to display ferns in the most natural setting, according to Shirley Hibberd in *The Fern Garden* –

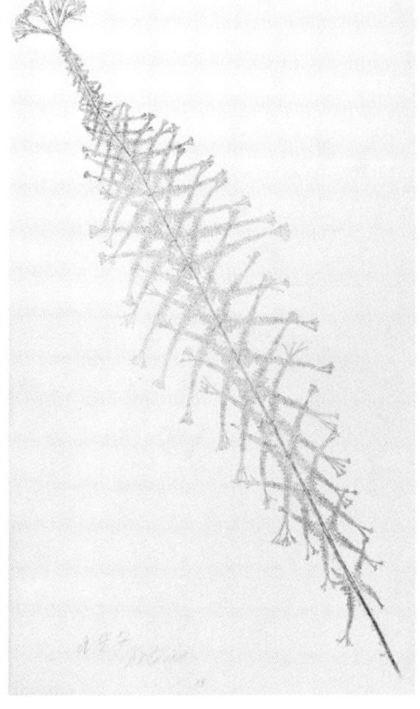

Main: A delicate variety of the soft shield fern (*Polystichum setiferum*). Photo: Mary Gibby/RBGE.

Right: A black and white nature print of *Athyrium filix-femina* var. *Victoriae* – 'a queen amongst lady ferns'. From Arthur Mowbray Jones, *Varieties of British Ferns*,1878.

WOODSIA ILVENSIS—*R. Br.*

OBLONG WOODSIA.

This is one of the rarest of British ferns, and one of the ornaments of our Moffat flora. Its small green fronds rise from a short round perennial rhizome, which is clothed with a few brown scales on the crown. The stem and rachis are covered with numerous pale scales or hairs. The stem is distinctly jointed at a short distance above the ground, at which joint the frond falls off in decay, leaving the lower part of the stem attached to the rhizome. The frond is from two to four inches long, of an oblong shape, tapering upwards. The pinnæ are generally opposite, of a thick and rigid texture, oblong in form and deeply lobed, the lowest lobe being largest: the upper surface of the frond is furnished with fine white hairs, and with these are mixed on the under surface a number of long brown hairy-like scales rising from the veins. Each lobe has an indistinct midvein with the lower venules forked, and the upper ones simple and less fertile. The venules extend quite free nearly to the margin, and bear the sori near their extremities. The sori are circular, and consist of a few spore cases seated on an indusium, which is a round membranaceous scale attached to the end of the venule. The margin of the indusium is split up into a number of jointed shining hairs which curve inwards, like a little cup, and cover the spore cases. These are almost sessile, and contain a number of rough oblong spores.

Above: A pressed plant of oblong woodsia (*Woodsia ilvensis*) in William Carruthers, *The Ferns of Moffat*, 1863.

"a garden with gravel walks amidst rocks and waterfalls, and on every bend the ferns present themselves in sheets of delicious verdure or in waving palm-like masses, or in a glorious confusion of brakes and lastrea intermingled as if the dryads themselves attended to the planting". John Birkenhead advises in *Ferns and Fern Culture,*" the most pleasing kind of fernery is that constructed in stone in the form of rockwork … or in the form of a glen, or ravine … in either case the paths should undulate, winding in and out, and should approach in appearance as near as possible a wild rocky pathway."

To support this passion for fern cultivation, not everyone would turn to nurserymen for their supplies: it was easier to plunder the countryside! For some it was the need to have examples of rare species in their collections, and so enthusiasts would travel far and wide. Localities of some of the rarest species were a closely guarded secret, as the least whisper could mean destruction. The first discovery of the rare Killarney bristle fern (*Trichomanes speciosum*) in Scotland was in 1863 by Robert Douglas, the 'walking postman' of Arran. His find was confirmed by the Edinburgh naturalist W. B. Simpson, who suggested that Douglas should keep the information secret. Douglas, however, showed the site to some gentlemen from Glasgow, one of whom, George Combe, returned and stripped the site almost bare. The evidence is to be found at RBGE, where annotated specimens from Arran are preserved in the Herbarium. Similarly, the Killarney fern was eradicated from one of its few sites in North Wales after the discoverer, J. Lloyd Williams, mentioned the locality to a friend.

Collection of plants from the wild was actively encouraged by the publication of a different form of fern book, one that provided descriptions of the different species but where illustrations were replaced by fragments of real specimens, or alternatively, by blank pages on which specimens could be mounted by the enthusiast. One such example in the RBGE Library, *The Ferns of Moffat*, not only gives details of localities where they could be found but also includes mounted dried specimens of all the listed species, both common and rare, including the rare oblong woodsia (*Woodsia ilvensis*) that had been discovered in the hills around Moffat. John Sadler, later a curator of RBGE, nearly lost his life trying to reach a tuft of this fern on a cliff near Moffat. The specimens he collected are preserved in the Herbarium at RBGE. When England and Scotland were finally connected by rail with the opening of the Caledonian Railway over Beattock summit in 1848, and a local branch line constructed into Moffat, what had been a remote area became easily accessible to many more visitors. Enthusiasts arrived in Moffat, private individuals collecting plants for their own herbaria and gardens, and fern dealers collecting for the horticultural trade; before long they did not need to comb the surrounding hills for specimens, but were met at the station by local hill shepherds offering plants for sale to the fern tourist. The woodsia populations were decimated.

As the passion for ferns continued, even the more common species suffered; Balfour, in 1870, reported that "The ferns in Arran are gathered in vast numbers, and nearly all the accessible specimens of the rarer species are taken away … we saw boys and women carrying large quantities of ferns taken up by the roots with a view of making a profit by the sale of them."

Pteridomania extended beyond the gardens, ferneries, Wardian cases and herbarium collections, and into the decorative arts. Ferns were celebrated in all types of decorated ware, in glass, pottery, metalwork, wood, paper and textiles, with fern ware making its first significant appearance at the 1862 International Exhibition in South Kensington. The great pottery manufacturers like Wedgwood, Adams and Dudson, were always alert to current fashion, and responded by introducing fern decoration to their already popular Jasperware, depicting raised, life-like fragments of British or exotic ferns, often set against a blue background.

Tea services were embellished in a similar fashion, or the fern motif may be more abstract, capturing fractal patterns, or unfurling crosiers. Terracotta was painted or enamelled with fern decoration, and ferns were engraved or etched onto glass.

Victorian fernware from the author's collection. **Clockwise from top left:** gold fern-decorated china; Dudson jasperware teapot; Mauchline fernware letter opener; and Wedgwood Jasperware biscuit barrel. Photos: Lynsey Wilson/RBGE.

Above: The Wedgwood memorial to William J. Hooker with fern decoration, in St Anne's Church, Kew Green, Surrey. Photo: Mary Gibby/RBGE and reproduced with kind permission of the vicar, Revd. Nigel Worn.

The firm of William and Andrew Smith of Mauchline, Ayrshire was producing a range of decorative wooden goods, usually referred to as 'Mauchline ware', and they included a design based on ferns. Pressed fronds were used as stencils; the image was gradually built up using a series of specimens, with the first-placed ones appearing darker in colour and the later, centremost specimens being much paler in colour.

The Coalbrookdale Company of Shropshire produced decorative cast ironware in 'ferny' designs, including a range of cast iron garden seats, usually painted in green or brown. Unfurling fronds embellished gravestones and ornamental garden stonework; the decorated urns at Dawyck Botanic Garden with an enfolding circle of fronds of the hart's tongue fern date from the 1840s, when Sir John Naesmyth brought in Italian labour to replace the house and ornamental garden stonework including steps, ball finials and urns.

Collections of mounted fern herbarium specimens were also turned into another example of the decorative arts, being bound in best morocco or even with carved wooden covers. Most of these beautiful volumes are based on collections of ferns from New Zealand or Darjeeling, each specimen artistically displayed on the right-hand page, usually annotated with the Latin name, but rarely with mention of the origin of the material. The collections had to be handled with care, as William Wells, of New Zealand, advised with his gift of such an album.

Wells' rules on handling fern books

If people are wise, for all are not fools,
They will pay strict attention to these rules
For if on the ferns they wish to look
They will commence at the finish of the book
rest the book on the table,
sit if they like, but stand if able
and to hold the book up with the left hand
allow the leaves to fall to the right
for by that means the ferns appear better to the sight
and if by these rules they do attend
the ferns will not break or loosen.

Left: Decorated urn from the 1840s at Dawyck Botanic Garden. Photo: Mary Gibby/RBGE.

Balfour's treasured collection

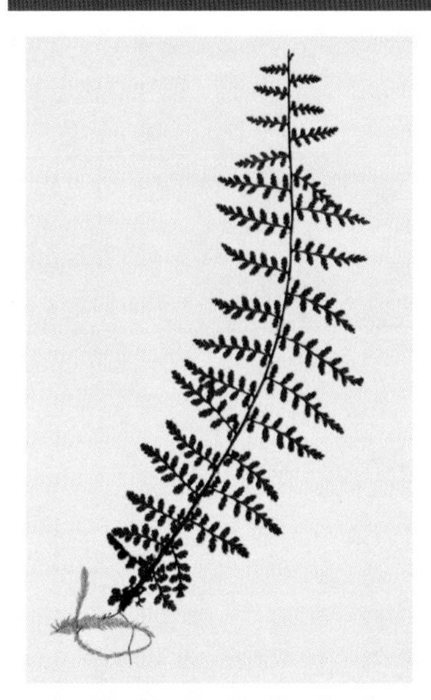

The Library at RBGE has an album of Scottish ferns collected in 1872 by Isaac Bayley Balfour, then a student at Edinburgh University. The 38 specimens were a Christmas gift for a family friend, Mrs Marjoribanks, and were obviously treasured by her as she had the collection bound in leather, and tooled with the title and her family initials. Isaac Bayley Balfour was the son of John Hutton Balfour and was to follow in his father's footsteps and become Regius Keeper at RBGE. In 1872, at the age of 19, he was awarded a student prize for his herbarium collection, and this collection of ferns may well represent part of his award-winning collection. As well as ferns local to Edinburgh, it includes some of the less common species from remote montane sites like Newman's alpine lady fern (*Athyrium distentifolium* var. *flexile*) above.

The Fernery at Benmore

The Benmore Fernery is a unique building in a remarkable setting. It occupies a remote site in Benmore Botanic Garden on a steep south west facing hillside, and a cliff on the eastern side forms an integral part of the structure. It was constructed in the early 1870s at the height of the Victorian fern craze, but went into decline in the early twentieth century and lay derelict for nearly a hundred years.

History

The Fernery was constructed for James Duncan, a wealthy sugar refiner. He purchased the Benmore Estate in 1870 and made many changes during the 1870s. He made additions to the main house, developed the walled garden with associated glasshouses (now demolished), and the stable block that now houses the Courtyard Gallery and garden offices. He also planted over six million trees, mainly conifers, across the estate. Adjacent to the house he built a large picture gallery for his extensive art collection that included contemporary works by the French Impressionists, and an experimental sugar refinery. In contrast, his heated Fernery was at some distance from the other buildings, in an area that had been recently planted with conifers. His picture gallery, sugar refinery and fernery have been described recently by architect Michael Thornley as "uncompromising buildings", "allied more closely to industrial rather than domestic styles of architecture of the time" and "strictly functional", although the setting of the Fernery on the side of the steep hillside, with its thick walls, towering south gable and curved glazed roof is extremely dramatic. Upkeep of the Fernery would have been a costly undertaking – glasshouses, with glazed sections supported on wooden frames and held in place by putty, were expensive to maintain and the coal-fired boiler must have needed attention daily.

With its south-west aspect, the highest level in the Fernery would have benefitted from sun for much of the day, while plants closer to the entrance, below the great south gable, would have

been in deep shade. From the vaulted entrance, the visitor would have entered this warm, humid environment to be greeted by a profusion of ferns in every direction: beside the paths, rising up beside the steps, suspended from the walls, and probably with the broad fronds of tree ferns silhouetted against the glazed roof. The paths and steps formed a figure of eight that provided a winding route for perambulation and exploration within the Fernery. We must imagine Duncan's visitors first marvelling at his stunning collection of paintings in the picture gallery and then being conveyed across his estate to his secret treasure house – the Fernery; climbing the steps to the small doorway at the foot of the massive gable end, entering the porch and emerging into a steamy, green paradise.

The Fernery nestles against the steep contour of the hillside. The site was probably chosen for its aspect, but it also meant that a small cliff could be incorporated into the structure, and the building has a striking position high above the valley floor. Shirley Hibberd, a horticulturist and editor of the *Gardener's Magazine*, provided long lists of ferns recommended for cultivation under different conditions in his book *The Fern Garden*, and advised on how to construct and lay out a fernery to achieve a natural effect, recommending building on a slope to gain from the range in temperature that could be realised in a heated fernery. Benmore Fernery reflected these recommendations. It is of large proportions with a rectangular plan and was originally covered by a glazed arched roof. The three thick walls, a long west wall and two barrel-vaulted gables are constructed of schist rubble and lime mortar, while the fourth wall is formed largely by the cliff itself. The Fernery's position at the side of a steep gulley means that its floor is on three levels; the uppermost (north) gable is fairly low – equivalent to one storey, whereas the lower (south) gable is massive, reflecting the considerable change in height within the building. On the west side, at the lower end of the long wall is a small lean-to building where the coal-fired boiler was housed. Remnants of the original roof of the Fernery showed that it was carried on iron semicircular trusses, supported on buttresses with substantial capping stones. The glazing had been supported in wooden overlapping frames, but the detailed structure of the frames was lost, and there was no trace of the

Facing page, top: The ruined Fernery building. Photo: Lynsey Wilson.

Left: The stable block and offices at Benmore Botanic Garden today. Photo: Peter Clarke/RBGE.

Above: Looking down on the restored Fernery, which was built into the steep slopes of this mountainside garden. Photo: Lynsey Wilson/RBGE.

'lantern' that ran along the ridge of the roof, other than the small gablets where it met the top of each rounded gable.

Access to the building was from the south, up the gulley by means of a winding path that was lined on each side with white quartz stones, and reaching a platform at the foot of the huge south gable. Visitors passed through the centrally placed door into the dark vaulted entrance porch and gained access via stairs on either side to the broad middle level, beside an ornamental grotto that arched over an oval pool. The paths were edged in white quartz and curved around the planting beds. To the left and right of the grotto two further sets of narrow stairs reached up to the highest level, under the short north gable and beside another fern bed constructed above the grotto. From all the walls of the Fernery cantilevered stones protruded, providing further platforms for plantings, while the damp, exposed cliff face inside the Fernery provided a further natural habitat. Hidden beside the paths were vents from the heating system, connected to an extensive network of underground pipes that had conducted warm air from the boiler below.

Not many miles from Benmore is another Victorian fernery. The fernery at Ascog Hall on the Isle of Bute was built only some eight years later than the Benmore Fernery, yet the contrast can hardly be greater. Both ferneries embrace the local topography, but whilst Benmore is a tall, solid structure that dominates the small gulley in which it is placed, Ascog fernery is in a different league in terms of architectural sophistication. It is wide and low, excavated into a gentle slope so that it is partially sunken, with the entrance down a few steps to a low door, and with the delicate glazed span roof reaching down to ground level at the upper side of the slope. A description and illustration of this fernery was published in *The Gardeners' Chronicle* in 1879, shortly after its completion, and included details of the layout and the fern collection. The fernery was unheated, yet had at least six different species of tree fern, including a specimen of the silver tree fern (*Cyathea dealbata*) some ten feet (3 metres) high. Remarkably, prior to Ascog's restoration in 1996, one of the original inhabitants was discovered – a specimen of *Todea barbara* with a massive rhizome a metre in diameter; reference to the same plant in 1879 suggested it was then already some 1,000 years old.

Main: Woodcut showing fernery at Ascog Hall, Isle of Bute. From *Gardeners' Chronicle*, October 25, 1879. Reproduced with kind permission from *Horticulture Week*.

Top: Ascog Hall fernery today. Photo: Virginia M. A. Nightingale.

Years of decline

Following the introduction of a German sugar bounty, Duncan became bankrupt and had to sell the estate in 1889. It was purchased by Henry John Younger as a sporting estate and he introduced an impressive collection of rhododendrons. The Fernery, being expensive to maintain, probably started into decline following the change of ownership, but, while the picture gallery and sugar refinery were demolished, the fabric of the Fernery remained, its isolated position perhaps helping to ensure its survival.

Through the generosity of Henry Younger's son, Harry George Younger, the Benmore estate was gifted to RBGE in 1925. The Fernery was already derelict by then and, although it was structurally maintained as long as was possible, some 15 years ago the building had to be closed to public access.

Unfortunately there are no written or visual records of the Fernery at Benmore in its heyday, no reports of the species under cultivation, nor any photographic archive, and so we can only speculate on the diversity of species that were cultivated. With exposure to the elements for probably a century, it is not surprising that the original collection of ferns has long since disappeared. Prior to restoration, with the roof open to the sky and for many years hidden away amongst tall trees, the Fernery at Benmore still lived up to its name as a fernery, having being invaded by a jumble of native species that luxuriated in the cool, moist and shady conditions. And in the year before restoration an exotic brittle bladder fern (*Cystopteris diaphana*) a species more commonly found in Madeira and the Azores, was discovered lurking in the grotto beside the pool. Could it have been one of the original denizens?

Clockwise from left: The steep climb up to the Fernery presented a challenge for the restoration team. Photo: Lynsey Wilson/RBGE; the original glazed roof was long gone when Benmore was gifted to RBGE. Photo: Lynsey Wilson/RBGE; native ferns colonised the derelict building. Photo: Michael Thornley.

Restoration of the Fernery at Benmore

In 1992 Historic Scotland designated the Fernery a Category B listed building as "a rare survival of this type of building ... [that] ... although it is ruinous, retains its walls and internal features. It is a rare structure and important as an integral part of the gardens at Benmore".

Listing the building proved to be a great stimulus for generating interest in the Fernery, and its restoration was championed by the Friends of Benmore and, in particular, by the Younger (Benmore) Trust. The Trust had been established by Harry G. Younger and in 1930 it had covered the running costs of the garden, but today it is used to support projects within the Garden. The Younger (Benmore) Trust was keen to see the structure maintained and so commissioned a feasibility study by MAST architects. The painstakingly detailed research and feasibility study revealed how the building had been constructed. The thick walls, tall gables, and lean-to boiler house appeared relatively unscathed. Much of the internal design was still evident even after a hundred years of decay, though the vault over the entrance had been demolished and details of its construction were sparse. There were remnants of the two staircases, one on each side of the porch, that curved outwards and upwards from the entrance; the grotto and pool had survived and there was evidence of

Left: The newly restored Fernery, showing the barrel-vaulted roof and the enormous gable wall to the south.

Right: Repairing the internal landscape and planting the first ferns.

Photos: Lynsey Wilson/RBGE.

the upper staircases that led above the grotto. High above, a few iron hoops that supported the original roof were still in place.

A meeting on site between the architect, Michael Thornley, and Historic Scotland was critical to establishing that total restoration was even feasible. To reconstruct the glazed roof to the original design using the rather insubstantial iron hoops and conventional wooden supports would have created enormous problems for long-term maintenance. However, as there was nothing left to indicate how the ridge-lantern had been constructed, nor how the structure was ventilated, it was possible to propose to, and win approval from, Historic Scotland for a new glazed barrel-vaulted roof constructed with modern materials. There was now a full restoration plan – all that was needed was to obtain the necessary funds. This was achieved with the support of significant donations by the Heritage Lottery Fund, the Younger (Benmore) Trust, the RBGE Members' Appeal and many personal donations.

Before work began it was essential to clear a number of trees that were adjacent to the site to provide access and to ensure that in the future the restored structure would not be damaged by falling trees. Restoration work started in May 2008. The site was secured and facilities brought in, including a crane that was needed to raise equipment from the work base at the bottom of the gulley up to the level of the Fernery. The first task focused on restoration of the walls, with scaffolding constructed inside and outside so that every area of wall could be cleared of vegetation and repointed. Despite heavy rain in October 2008, work progressed well during the autumn, and the final critical measurements could be made to allow accurate construction of the metal arches to support the new roof glazing. By Christmas most of the glazing was in place. With the glazed roof and lantern in place, the internal scaffolding could be removed to allow work to start inside the Fernery, rebuilding the vault over the entrance, repairing the grotto, re-instating the paths and steps, and recreating the water supply.

There is no electricity in the building; the ventilation in the lantern is operated manually and the water supply relies on a gravity feed. The barrel-vaulted roof has a curved ladder on each side to provide access for maintenance, and these ladders can be cranked manually to move them between the gables. The completed structure, with the newly restored walls, wall heads protected by thick lead flashings and the newly constructed glazed roof, is sounder today than when it was first erected in 1870 – and this bodes well for its future.

Plantings – forest ferns of the world

The ferns on display are from many parts of the world, and have been selected for their diversity of form, as well as the diversity of their origins. Most have been grown from spores at RBGE, and over 75% are of known wild origin. All are from temperate or warm temperate regions, with many from the southern hemisphere. They include species native to the Juan Fernandez Islands; this is an island group in the Pacific Ocean off the coast of Chile that includes Robinson Crusoe Island where Alexander Selkirk was marooned for over four years, giving rise to the subsequent tale by Daniel Defoe. Other ferns are from the Azores, Hawaii, South Africa, New Zealand and Tasmania; some are now rare in the wild and in need of conservation protection.

RBGE Horticulturist Andrew Ensoll has used his knowledge and long practical experience of fern cultivation to create the design of the plantings within the Fernery. Perhaps the most spectacular are the tree ferns – the tall, slender *Dicksonia squarrosa* above the vaulted entrance is from the South Island of New Zealand. *Cyathea gleichenioides* opposite the grotto is from Papua New Guinea and *Cyathea cooperi*, towering above the grotto, is from Australia. The crosiers and stipes of *Dicksonia* species are covered in long hairs, whereas in *Cyathea* they have a dense covering of scales. *Cyathea princeps* from the mountains of Central America has beautiful pale to golden scales that contrast markedly with the bright green fronds. Two species of *Cyathea* are from South Africa: *Cyathea capensis* can be recognised by the very finely dissected 'fuzz' of small fronds that envelope the crown, whereas *Cyathea dregei* has a stocky trunk and in the wild can grow in full sun. *Cibotium* and *Culcita* are characterised by the dense covering of soft hairs on the stipe bases. In the small tree ferns, *Cibotium schiedei* from Mexico and *Cibotium menziesii* from Hawaii, this takes the form of thick yellowish or brown 'wool', whilst *Culcita macrocarpa*, from the Azores to Spain and Portugal, has soft, rusty brown, fine hairs on the stipe bases.

Beside the steps leading up from entrance on the east side is the rare *Thyrsopteris elegans*, an endemic fern of Juan Fernandez Islands, and plants of South African *Todea barbara* grown from spores from the massive 1,000-year-old specimen at Ascog Hall fernery. The delicate Japanese *Adiantum pedatum* occupies the understorey opposite, easily identified by the wiry black stipes and delicate small fan-shaped frond segments. The two plants of hard shield fern (*Polystichum aculeatum*) that cling to the damp, exposed cliff colonised this position when the Fernery was derelict and have survived the restoration work. The grotto itself provides the ideal conditions for sheltering filmy ferns including the rare Killarney bristle fern (*Trichomanes speciosum*).

Blechnum species occupy the higher levels, below the tree ferns. The handsome *Blechnum cycadifolium* is known only from the Juan Fernandez Islands, where it grows in the low forest zone together with *Pteris berteroana*, while *Blechnum palmiforme* is from Gough Island in the South Atlantic.

Many ferns produce branching, creeping rhizomes and this gives them the ability to expand into large patches, to colonise mossy boulders, tree trunks – even the trunks of tree ferns. In the Fernery they form ideal ground cover and are planted on some of the many stone ledges – *Rumohra berteroana* from the southern hemisphere, the small, simple-fronded *Pyrrosia eleagnifolia* from New Zealand or the palmate-fronded *Pyrrosia polydactylis*; *Oleandra wallichii* from Nepal and *Phymatosorus diversifolius* from Tasmania.

Variety of form is provided by plantings of fern allies such as giant horsetails from Chile, *Equisetum giganteum*, and spike mosses, *Selaginella* species, plants with tiny leaves and creeping rhizomes that provide good ground cover.

Left: RBGE staff preparing the beds for planting.
Clockwise from top left: *Sadleria cyatheoides*; *Histiopteris incisa*; *Arachniodes simplicior*; fern plantings above the grotto; an unfurling frond.
Photos: Mary Gibby/RBGE.

Fern highlights in RBGE's four Gardens

Benmore

A range of the native ferns that are characteristic of Scotland's western woodlands can be found growing naturally at Benmore, enjoying the benefits of the southern aspect, shaded gullies and natural rock outcrops, as well as the suitable climate with a high annual rainfall of 2 - 3,000 mm, cool summer temperatures and mild winters.

Beyond the Fernery, Benmore is home to British native ferns of the Atlantic oakwoods, such as the hard fern (*Blechnum spicant*), lady fern (*Athyrium filix-femina*), male fern (*Dryopteris filix-mas*) and particularly the scaly male ferns (*Dryopteris affinis* agg). Scattered individuals of the hay-scented buckler fern (*Dryopteris aemula*) flourish on steep south- and west-facing slopes, beside rock outcrops and close to water courses. Ferns native to the Azores thrive here too, including *Dryopteris crispifolia* with related species and hybrids. Fern plantings reflect the geographical arrangement at Benmore – Chilean species in the Chilean Rainforest Glade including *Lophosoria quadripinnata*, and species from Tasmania on the hillside above the Fernery, with Japanese ferns to the east. A large stand of the ostrich fern (*Matteuccia struthiopteris*) fills the flat boggy ground below the Fernery gulley. Polypodies thrive on branches of the large sycamore close to Benmore House, whilst maidenhair and black spleenworts (*Asplenium trichomanes* and *Asplenium adiantum-nigrum*) have colonised mortared walls.

From top: Tree ferns flourish again inside the Fernery. Photo: Mary Gibby/RBGE; hay scented buckler fern (*Dryopteris aemula*). Photo: Vlasta Jamnický/RBGE; hard fern (*Blechnum spicant*). Photo: Vlasta Jamnický/RBGE.
Below: Native ferns in profusion on a cliff at Benmore. Photo: Lynsey Wilson/RBGE.

Dawyck

On entering the Garden in spring, visitors are greeted by dense stands of the pale green ostrich fern (*Matteuccia struthiopteris*) unfurling their fronds in dappled sunlight beneath the trees. It flourishes in damp hollows close to Scrape Burn, whilst in drier areas among trees and shrubs there are dark green stands of the stiff-fronded sword fern (*Polystichum* aff. *munitum*) from the Pacific North West, carpets of American oak fern (*Gymnocarpium dryopteris*) and the southern hemisphere dwarf hard fern (*Blechnum penna-marina*). Some of the ornamental urns beside the stone steps are decorated with overlapping fern fronds that look very like those of the hart's tongue fern; the stone steps, ball finial and urns were the work of Italian craftsmen in the 1840s. From the Dutch-style bridge a profusion of ferns can be seen growing beside the tumbling burn: ostrich and sword fern again, native male ferns and lady fern, and also magnificent stands of royal fern, (*Osmunda regalis*). *Woodsia ilvensis*, the rare woodsia from the Scottish Borders, is included in Dawyck's rare plant trail, and it thrives on the bank above the path on the east side of the burn. Heron Wood, the cryptogamic garden – rich in mushrooms and toadstools, lichens, mosses and liverworts – is home to some British native woodland ferns, but also includes species and hybrids of hardy *Dryopteris* from North America and Europe.

Right: The ostrich fern (*Matteuccia struthiopteris*) beside one of Dawyck's ornamental urns. Photo: Lynsey Wilson/RBGE.

Main and right: The splendour of the Ferns and Fossils House in Edinburgh's Glasshouses. Photos: Lynsey Wilson/RBGE.

Edinburgh

The Edinburgh Garden has rich warm temperate and tropical collections under glass. The Ferns and Fossils House is dominated by a diversity of tree ferns: towering specimens of *Cyathea* and *Dicksonia*, the rare *Dicksonia arborescens* from St Helena and *Cibotium barometz* from eastern Asia. Epiphytic staghorn ferns (*Platycerium* species), are suspended on the glazed wall by the entrance. Large specimens of *Marattia* and *Angiopteris* thrive in the humid atmosphere, while creeping *Selaginella* species form good ground cover. The north west corner of the fern house is dominated by *Equisetum myriochaetum* from South America, a horsetail some three metres in height. The Temperate Palm House is home to a large stand of *Dryopteris crispifolia*, whilst an extensive patch of *Rumohra adiantiformis*, the florists' fern, grows against the external north side of the fern house.

The trail through the Woodland Garden leads past a variety of native species, particularly male ferns and lady fern; extensive drifts of the royal fern are found near the main pond, with plantings of *Polystichum* and *Dryopteris* species among the rhododendrons. The Rock Garden features smaller species – spleenworts and polypodies.

Logan

Logan celebrates southern hemisphere ferns. The plantings of the Tasmanian tree fern *(Dicksonia antarctica)* in the Walled Garden have long been one of the iconic images of Scotland's 'most tropical garden'. With less severe frosts over recent years, an effective shelter belt and the warm moist air influenced by the Gulf Stream, tree ferns are flourishing at Logan; to quote the Curator, "*Dicksonia antarctica* is now one of our most frequent weeds"!

A new understorey forest of *Dicksonia antarctica* and *Dicksonia fibrosa* has been planted in the Tasmanian Glade, below gum trees (*Eucalyptus* species) and tea trees (*Leptospermum*). Nearby is a range of ferns from Chile and the Juan Fernandez Islands, the finely dissected *Lophosoria quadripinnata*, the tree fern *Thyrsopteris elegans* and the magnificent hard fern *Blechnum cycadifolium*. Other southern hemisphere ferns are planted within the Walled Garden or hide in the shade of the lower south woodland including several tree ferns – *Cyathea dregei* from South Africa, *Cyathea smithii* and the New Zealand sporting emblem *Cyathea dealbata* that is silvery white on the underside of the fronds. Macaronesian species from the Azores and Madeira flourish here too – *Culcita macrocarpa, Dryopteris crispifolia, Arachniodes webbianum* and *Woodwardia radicans*.

Above: The view over the Tasmanian Glade. Photo: Mary Gibby/RBGE.

Below: New plantings of *Cyathea* in the Walled Garden, with *Dicksonia* in the background. Photo: Mary Gibby/RBGE.

A few species are still under threat from collectors for their 'useful' produce. The fibrous 'trunks' of tree ferns have been used in the cultivation of epiphytic orchids. Some species of tree ferns, *Cyathea* and *Dicksonia*, now have international protection by CITES, the Convention on International Trade in Endangered Species of Wild Fauna and Flora. Other tree ferns have been exploited for medicinal purposes. The bizarre 'Vegetable Lamb of Tartary' (*Cibotium barometz*) from China and South East Asia, gets is name from the dense 'wool' of fine hairs on the stipe bases and rhizome; in medieval times it was believed to grow sheep as its fruit! These dense hairs are used as an ingredient in Traditional Chinese Medicine, and so this species has also been included in the CITES list of protected species. The 'fur' from plants of *Culcita macrocarpa* from the Azores and Madeira was collected for use in hot poultices on wounds to promote healing.

At RBGE the skills of the horticulturist have been critical to the development of the extensive living collections of ferns at all four Gardens; rather than being collected from the wild, many of the magnificent ferns in the collections at Benmore, Edinburgh and Logan have been cultivated from spores. By propagating ferns from spores, substantial *ex situ* populations can be established; at the same time knowledge is gained of their cultivation requirements. Some 80% ferns in the living collections at RBGE are of wild origin, and this includes many that are threatened in the wild.

Above: RBGE botanists monitoring a reintroduction site for the oblong woodsia. Photo: Mary Gibby/RBGE.

Left: The conservation collection of oblong woodsia at the Edinburgh Garden. Photo: Heather McHaffie/RBGE.

Fern conservation

By far the greatest threat to fern populations today is habitat loss and fragmentation, compounded by the effects of changing climate.

Research at RBGE

In Britain over-collecting by the amateur fern enthusiast is happily a thing of the past and some of the more common ferns of Britain and Ireland have re-established flourishing and extensive populations. However, some of our rarer ferns populations were either totally eliminated from some sites or reduced to very low numbers of plants that have failed to reproduce successfully, and have continued their decline.

RBGE is engaged in a number of fern research projects in Britain and abroad, from the conservation of *Woodsia ilvensis* in the UK to an identification guide for ferns in Thailand.

Above, left to right: A healthy reintroduction of oblong woodsia in northern England. Photo: Mary Gibby/RBGE; Thai ferns – *Dipteris conjugata* and *Pyrrosia lanceolata*. Photos: David Middleton/RBGE.
Below: RBGE botanist Stuart Lindsay under a large plant of *Cibotium barometz* in Thailand. Photo: Preecha Karaket/Forest Herbarium Bangkok.

The oblong woodsia

There are now fewer than a hundred plants surviving in scattered sites in upland areas of England, Scotland and Wales, and the species is included in the UK's Biodiversity Action Plans for conservation. Regular monitoring of a population at one of the last sites for the species near Moffat recorded a gradual reduction from about twenty-five plants in 1954 down to just three remaining in 1999. There was clearly need for action. Why did the population continue to decline? Although individual plants can be fairly long-lived, there seemed to be no evidence of successful reproduction in this small population, no establishment of new plants, and individual clumps were gradually being lost, probably the result of rock fall from the crumbling cliff on which they grew, from disturbance by browsing animals or as a consequence of summer droughts. Licences were obtained from the conservation agencies, Scottish Natural Heritage (SNH), English Nature (now Natural England, NE) and the Countryside Council for Wales (CCW), to collect spores from all of the populations in Britain. Experimental work in Edinburgh showed that the spores were viable and that new plants could be established. With the approval and encouragement of the conservation agencies, a plan was developed to introduce new populations at a few sites where the species had been lost. Re-introductions began in 1999. All populations are monitored regularly and there is almost 100% survival at three of the five sites and 35% of the plants at the other two sites.

The ferns of Thailand

Tropical forests provide a rich environment for ferns, and so it is not surprising that while Britain has about 73 native species, the ferns of Thailand number some 670. The diversity and abundance of ferns in tropical forest can be used to monitor the 'health' of a forest, but specialist skills are needed to identify material. Research at RBGE is developing an online key to the ferns of Thailand that will provide a user-friendly guide so that fern identification can be carried out not only by botanists but also by ecologists, conservationists and forest managers.

Left: The polypodies are epiphytes; their rhizomes creep amongst mosses on large boulders or high on the trunks and branches of trees. Photo: Laurie Campbell.

Scotland's Atlantic woodlands and their ferns

The Atlantic oak and birch woods of western Scotland are recognised internationally for their rich diversity of mosses, liverworts and lichens. Much of this woodland is found close to the sea, often on steep slopes or on the cliffs above raised beaches. Ferns thrive in these shaded woodlands where there is high rainfall, relatively mild temperatures and clean air. They grow in dappled or deep shade, in deep damp soils, amongst mossy boulders, on rocky slopes, in gullies and beside burns.

Sweet mountain fern

In damper areas or beside burns the sweet mountain fern (*Oreopteris limbosperma*) is found – so-called because of the sweet lemon smell that is released when the fronds are crushed. This is an erect shuttlecock fern, with pale green fronds that taper markedly towards the base.

Right: Sweet mountain fern (*Oreopteris limbosperma*). Photo: Mary Gibby/RBGE.

Above: Hard fern (*Blechnum spicant*). Photo: Vlasta Jamnický/RBGE.

Hard fern

The common hard fern (*Blechnum spicant*) grows in acidic soils. It has a rosette of spreading, long and narrow, once-dissected, leathery, dark glossy-green, sterile fronds and a number of stiff, upright, fertile fronds, also long and narrow but with narrower segments.

Buckler ferns

Buckler ferns are widespread; these ferns are characterised by their thrice-dissected fronds and their kidney-shaped sori. Broad buckler fern (*Dryopteris dilatata*) the most common species, has a wide, spreading shuttlecock, fairly broad fronds and at the base of the stipe has brown scales with a dark brown or black central stripe. It grows on slopes and amongst rocks, whereas the narrow buckler fern (*Dryopteris carthusiana*) tolerates wetter ground conditions and is frequent in wet woodland on flatter, boggy ground. Often in these areas the two species appear to grow together, but the broad buckler fern is confined to drier hummocks or adjacent sloping ground. The narrow buckler fern has a creeping root-stock and can be recognised by its narrower, upright, paler green fronds, and the scales at the base of the stipe are always very pale green or brown and never have a darker central stripe.

The northern buckler fern (*Dryopteris expansa*) grows in the high corries of the Scottish mountains but can also be found close to sea level in the wet, western woodlands. Here it may be difficult to distinguish from the broad buckler fern, but it is usually slightly paler green in colour, more finely dissected and the stipe scales are gingery brown, sometimes with a narrow darker stripe.

The hay-scented buckler fern, (*Dryopteris aemula*) is characteristic of Atlantic woodland. It is luxuriant in the woods of western Scotland, growing on boulder-strewn slopes or in more open sites at the heads of gullies, usually at fairly low altitude. The species is distinguished from other buckler ferns as it has a lax shuttlecock, a more triangular frond and dark stipe, and thrice-dissected fronds have a 'crisped' appearance, curling upwards along the edges. The smell of hay – coumarin – is released when the frond is crushed.

Below: Broad buckler fern (*Dryopteris dilatata*). Photo: Vlasta Jamnický/RBGE.

Shield ferns

Shield fern (*Polystichum* species) thrive where there are base-rich soils. They form lax shuttlecocks with twice-pinnate fronds and are readily distinguished from male and buckler ferns by the peltate or shield-shaped indusium and the long spines on the ultimate segments. The fronds of the hard shield fern (*Polystichum aculeatum*) are leathery and taper towards the base of the frond, while fronds of the soft shield fern (*Polystichum setiferum*) have a softer texture and a broader base.

Left: A hard shield fern (*Polystichum aculeatum)* with forked tips to the fronds. Photo: Mary Gibby/RBGE.

Lady fern (see photo inside front cover)

The delicate lady fern (*Athyrium filix-femina*) has a shuttlecock of paler green and twice- or thrice-dissected fronds that may reach a metre in height. In some individuals the fronds have a light green stipe and rachis, in others these may be reddish brown, and mixed populations are not infrequent. As the day length shortens in autumn and the temperature falls, the fronds of the lady fern soon wither.

Male fern (see page 14)

The male fern (*Dryopteris filix-mas*) and scaly male ferns (*Dryopteris affinis*, *borreri* and *cambrensis*) all have a more robust appearance than the delicate lady fern.
The fronds are bipinnate and form large, erect shuttlecocks; the species are differentiated by their scales and the shape of the pinnule lobes. They thrive where the ground is drier or among boulders.

Hart's tongue fern

Most spleenworts are small rock ferns. The hart's tongue fern (*Asplenium scolopendrium*) is larger and flourishes on the woodland floor. It is easily recognised by its long, narrow, strap-like fronds, bright green in colour. It favours base-rich soils and will colonise mortared walls.

Below and centre: The beech fern (*Phegopteris connectilis*) and oak fern (*Gymnocarpium dryopteris*) are small creeding ferns that form large colonies on well drained soils. Photo: Mary Gibby/RBGE.

Below: Hart's tongue fern (*Asplenium scolopendrium*). Photo: Vlasta Jamnický/RBGE.

Above: Tunbridge filmy fern (*Hymenophyllum tunbrigense*). Photo: Mary Gibby/RBGE.

Filmy ferns

Our three native filmy ferns need shade, high humidity and protection from frost – conditions that are found within the moist Atlantic woodlands and in sheltered gullies close to the coast. The filmy ferns get their name from their very delicate fronds that are only one cell thick. *Hymenophyllum tunbrigense* and Wilson's filmy fern (*Hymenophyllum wilsonii*) are found close by Benmore in Puck's Glen. Tunbridge filmy fern has small fronds, less than 10 cm long; Wilson's filmy fern is longer and narrower, and both often grow amongst mosses.

The Killarney bristle fern

The Killarney bristle fern (*Trichomanes speciosum*) is one of Britain's rarest ferns and is protected under the Wildlife and Countryside Act (Schedule 8) and Habitats Directive. It suffered drastically from over-collecting during the Victorian period.

As its name implies, a stronghold for the species is in western Ireland, and it flourishes in Madeira and the Azores. It needs deep shade and high humidity, and is often found close to running water at low elevations. Britain is at the northern limit of its range and here it rarely produces spores but, with its creeping rhizome, it can slowly expand and extend in size. In recent years, free-growing gametophytes of the Killarney fern have been identified. These are not the prothalli typical of most ferns; the spores produce a branched filamentous gametophyte with the appearance of green baize; its occurrence had been overlooked. It was first recorded at sites of old records of the Killarney fern or close to colonies of *Hymenophyllum tunbrigense*, but more extensive surveys have revealed that, unlike the sporophyte that is largely confined to western Britain and Ireland, the gametophytes can be found in deep crevices protected from frost, from the north of Scotland to the south coast of England. Conservation plans for the species in Britain included proposals for re-introductions to sites where it had been lost, but these have now been rejected with the knowledge that gametophyte populations are present at these sites; this local, growing 'spore bank' will allow the opportunity for natural colonisation, especially as the climate becomes warmer and wetter.

Right: Killarney bristle fern (*Trichomanes speciosum*). Photo: Mary Gibby/RBGE.

Left: Royal fern in May (*Osmunda regalis*). Photo: Mary Gibby/RBGE.

Royal fern

The royal fern (*Osmunda regalis*) is another species that thrives in western Britain, not in deep woodland but in more open habitats, in damp ground, often on stream banks and in gullies. It can be distinguished from other native species by the spore bearing tassel at the apex of the frond. Delicate, pale brownish-green fronds unfurl in May and their bright green tips reveal the developing sporangia. The rootstock becomes massive with age. Many sites of this species have been lost, partly through over-collecting, but also through change in habitat where wetland has been drained. However, the plants have a great ability to reproduce and spread, especially along suitable watercourses.

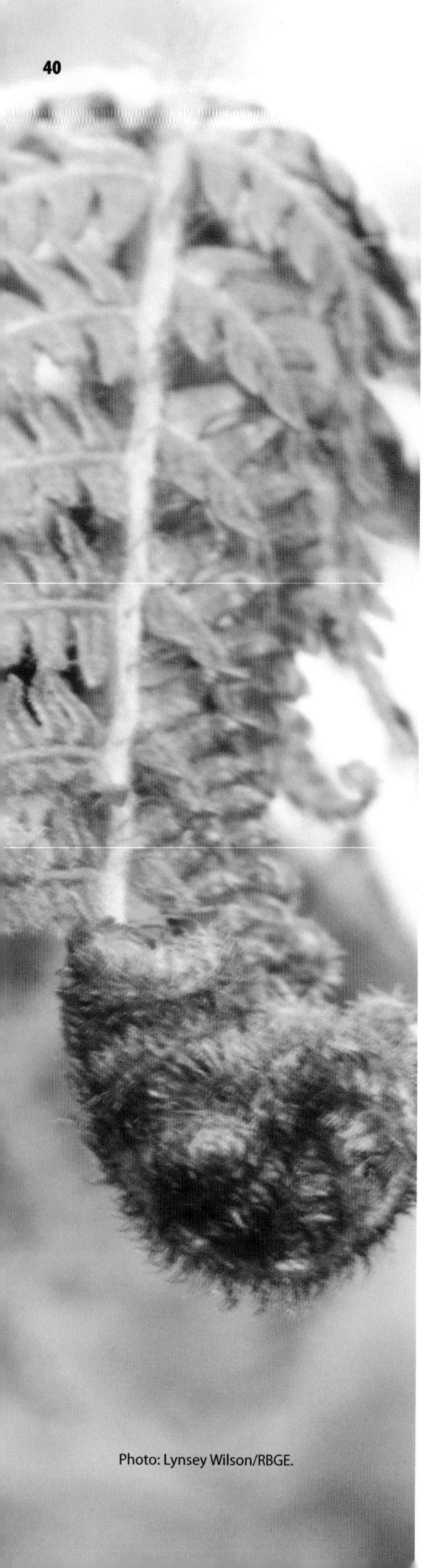

Photo: Lynsey Wilson/RBGE.

Finding out more about ferns

The Royal Botanic Garden Edinburgh has a regular programme of courses on fern identification, ranging from one-day to short-term residential courses – details are available at **www.rbge.org.uk/whats-on**

The Field Studies Council organises residential courses on ferns – information is available at **www.field-studies-council.org/**

The British Pteridological Society encourages the appreciation, conservation, cultivation and scientific study of ferns, horsetails, clubmosses and quillworts. It has an active programme of national and regional meetings, including discussion meetings and field meetings, publishes books, journals and a magazine, and provides small grants for the study of ferns. Fern World, the web site of the British Pteridological Society, is at **www.nhm.ac.uk/hosted_sites/bps/**

Ascog Hall Victorian Fernery and Gardens and on the Isle of Bute is open from Easter to October. For further information see **www.ascoghallfernery.co.uk** or contact Mrs Susannah Alcorn, Ascog Hall, Ascog, Isle of Bute PA20 9EU. Tel: 01700 504555; email: office@ascoghallfernery.co.uk

Recommended books on ferns

Ferns (RHS Wisley Handbook) by Martin Rickard. Mitchell Beazley, 2008.

Gardening with ferns by Martin Rickard. David and Charles PLC, 2005.

Encyclopedia of Garden Ferns by Sue Olsen. Timber Press, 2007.

Fern Growers Manual: Revised and Expanded Edition by Barbara Joe Hoshizaki and Robbin C. Moran. Timber Press, 2001.

A Natural History of Ferns by Robbin C. Moran. Timber Press, 2004.

Fern Guide: A Field Guide to the Ferns, Clubmosses, Quillworts and Horsetails of the British Isles (AIDGAP), 3rd Revised Edition. James Merryweather and Michael Hill. Field Studies Council (FSC), 2007.

Key to common ferns (Ferns chart) by James Merryweather. Field Studies Council (FSC), 2005.

The Ferns of Britain and Ireland, 2nd Edition by C.N. Page. Cambridge University Press, 1997.

Photo: Mary Gibby/RBGE.